Spike the Dragon

Written by Lisa Thompson
Pictures by Andy and Inga Hamilton

Spike the dragon was not like other dragons.

3

Other dragons' caves were dark and spooky.

The blue dragon's cave was very dark and very spooky.

Not Spike's cave!

Spike's cave was full of candles.

"The more light the better," said Spike.

Other dragons' caves were dusty and dirty.

The green dragon's cave was very dusty and full of dirt.

Not Spike's cave!

Spike's cave was clean and tidy.

"I can't stand mess," said Spike.

11

Other dragons looked after their treasure all day.

The yellow dragon counted his treasure every day.

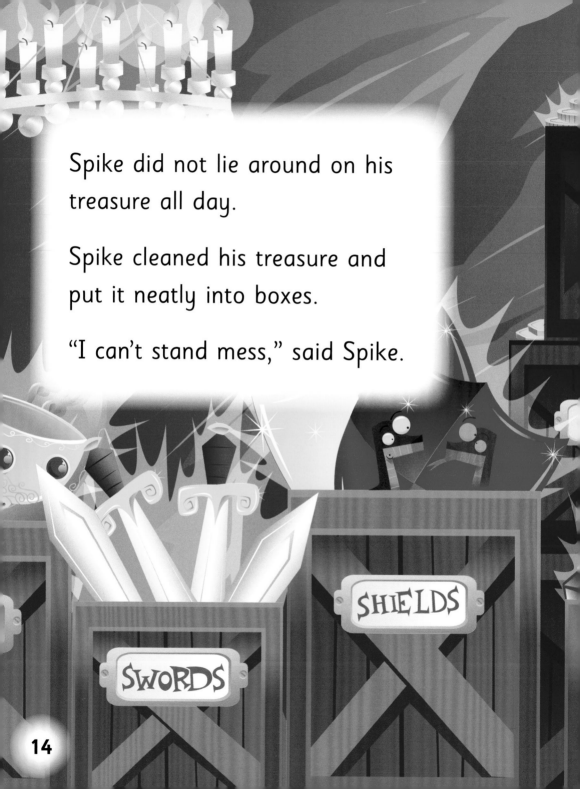

Spike did not lie around on his treasure all day.

Spike cleaned his treasure and put it neatly into boxes.

"I can't stand mess," said Spike.

SWORDS

SHIELDS

15

"Are you like other dragons at all?" asked Eric the Knight.

"Oh yes!" smiled Spike.

"I always catch the knights who visit me," said Spike.

He asked Eric to sit on a chair.

18

Spike did not eat knights like other dragons.

He let them go after they ate dinner with him.

20

Every year the knights had a party to say thank you to Spike.

There were lots of gifts and songs. Everyone danced.

Spike was not like other dragons.

Spike was their friend.

23